Level 1

Duet Favorites

by Jane Smisor Bastien

Contents

KJOS WEST · Neil A. Kjos. Jr. Publisher · San Diego. California

ISBN 0-8497-5091-1

Bulldog Blues

Secondo

Moderate blues tempo

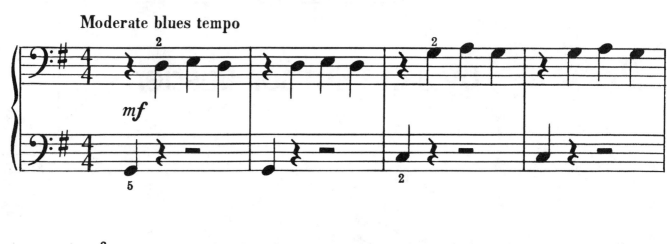

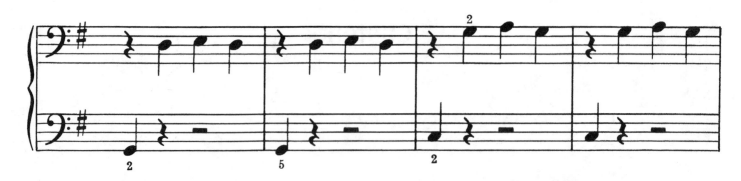

Inter. Copyright Secured   All Rights Reserved
Printed in U.S.A.

WP60

Bulldog Blues

Primo

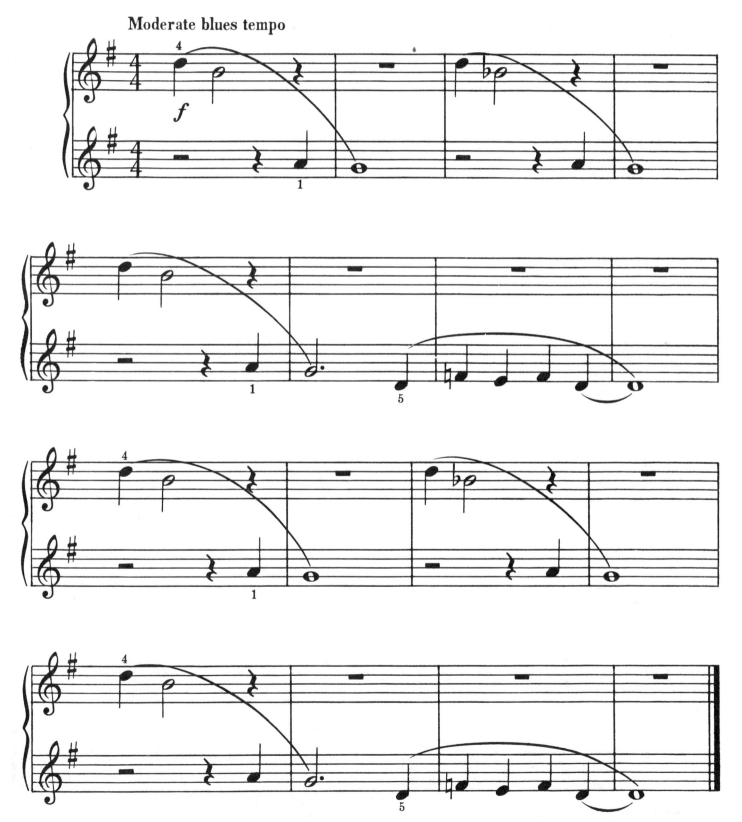

Ghost Dance

Secondo

Moderato

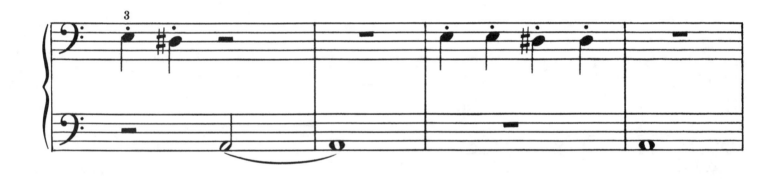

Ghost Dance

Primo

Skip to My Lou

Secondo

Folk Song

With spirit

Skip to My Lou

Primo

Folk Song

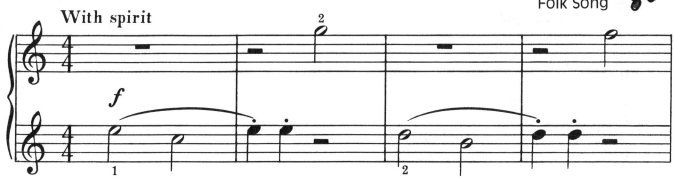

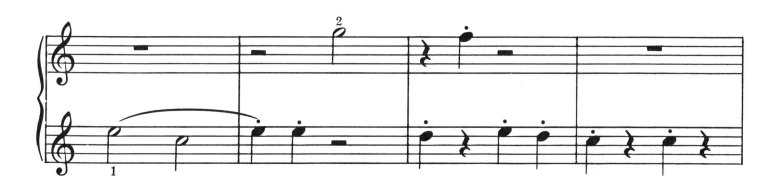

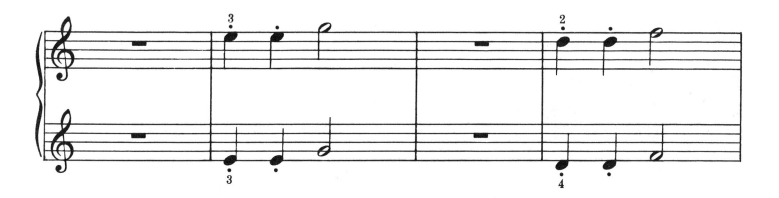

Promenade

Secondo

Promenade

Primo

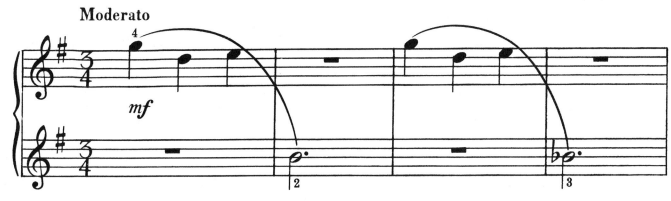

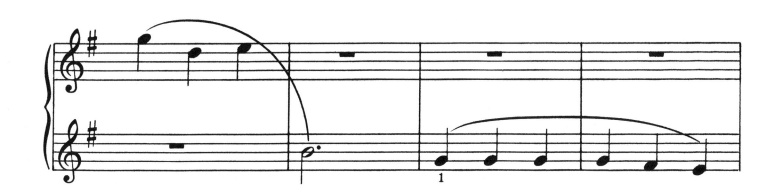

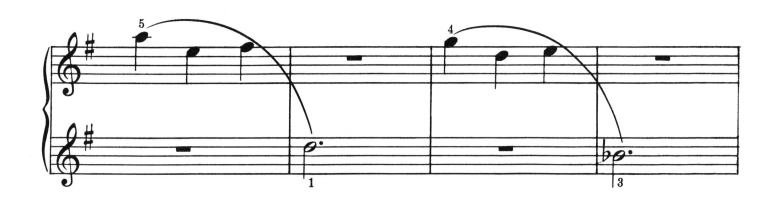

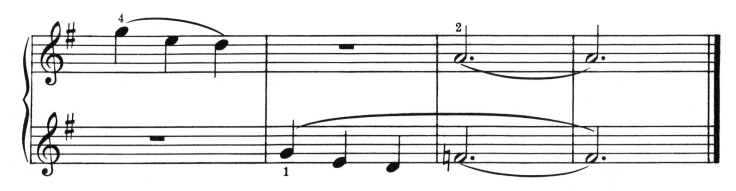

Comin' Round the Mountain

Secondo

Folk Song

Comin' Round the Mountain

Primo

Folk Song

Sailor's Song

Secondo

Sailor's Song

Primo

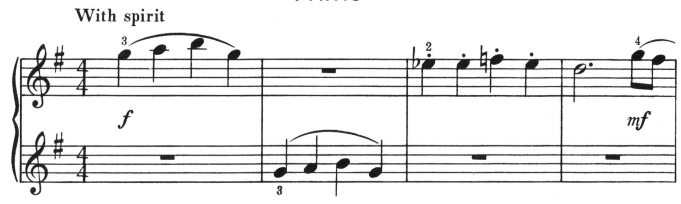

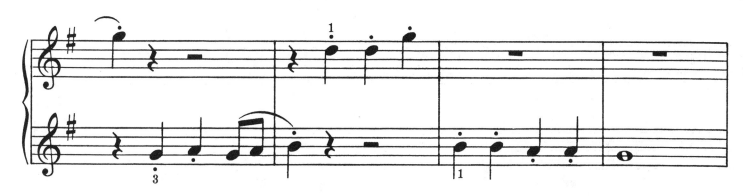

POP PIANO STYLES

A light and refreshing collection of rock, blues, boogie, and disco styles from Jane and James Bastien. From foot-stompin' rhythms to melancholy moods, these up-to-date sounds encourage practicing and performing for pianists of all ages!

Levels 1-4

Level 1
WP51

Level 2
WP52

Level 3
WP53

Level 4
WP54